TO SHAWN UNSHAVENLY THINE BABY GRAMPS '95

Artis

Shawn Bubble Magic! No Illusions! Real Magic! Love is! Tom Noddy

Hup hip ho! Dmitri

YO Shawn,
It's good we connect.
Thanks for savin lives, Bro.
You're the man.
Forever Yours,
Artis

THE ONE HUNDRED YEAR COMMITTEE, IN ENGLAND, LONG ABOUT 1960, COMBINED THE LETTERS "N" AND "D" IN THE LANGUAGE OF SEMAPHORE, TO DIMINISH THE PROSPECTS OF WAR, AND REPRESENT NUCLEAR DISARMAMENT ☮

Artis

ASPIRATIONS TO MANIFESTATIONS

from the Womb to the Void

Hulogosi
Eugene 1993

Photo Guru, Tom Holt

Cover art by RF Russell Company

Book design by Alan Trist

Printed in the United States of America

 Printed on acid-free, recycled paper

---

LIBRARY OF CONGRESS CATALOGING-IN-PUBLICATION DATA:

Artis, 1948-

Aspirations to manifestations : from the womb to the void / Artis.

p. cm.

ISBN 0-938493-20-5 (alk. paper) : $13.50

I. Title.

PS3551.R78A9 1993

811'.54--dc20 93-8430

CIP

HULOGOSI, P.O. BOX 1188, EUGENE, OREGON 97440 ● (503) 688-1199

I AM THE WORLD

by Katie Hinde (ten years old, 1990)

I am the world
I am the future
I am the decision maker
I am the world
I am the peace

I am the love
I am the freedom
I am the world

I am the history
I am the history to come
I am the was
I am the will be
I am the world

I am the war
I am the fears
I am the death
I am the tears
I am the world

I am the hunger
I am the disease
I am the shadows
I am the breeze
I am the world

I am the water
I am the sky
I am the fish
I am the birds that fly
I am the world

I am culture
I am custom
I am the arts
I am the theatre
I am the world

I am me
I am you
I am what you see
I am the world

Table of

Contents

Dedicated to Mom for daring to not conform and keeping the knowledge of fun foremost in all plans; to Walt Haines for designing and manufacturing "musical spoons" in the mid 50's and to Lawrence Welk for funding that project for ten years. All three of these people had conspicuous and contagious faith in music, fun, and exhaustive determination.

My gratitude to Joan and the millions of you who have supported me and continue to support me.

Prologue

WHEN people ask me, "Where are you from?" (regardless of the language), I respond "Mom, my mother." Regardless of our relationship, the differences, the harmony, the joy, or misery, the truth is, she bore me and suffered me first.

I am *from* my mother, Penny Bliss. *For* myself, naturally. *Of* this planet, obviously. And undeniably *influenced* by the culture most immediately about me, i.e., family, community and nation.

When I was born, in Kodiak, Alaska, October 3, 1948, at 7:45 AM, my father, Leroy Wensel, and mother named me Roger Leroy Wensel. According to Mom, my father "couldn't bring the check home for drinking it." That was, as his mother said, "what World War II did to him." Consequently, Mom left with me. We came "outside" (left Alaska), when I was five months old and settled in Seattle just in time for a notorious earthquake of that era.

I know little of my father. He was a lineman, born on December 25, but I don't know what year. Probably in the very early '20s. The only photo I've ever seen of him is with him on a telephone pole from a distance of approximately 50 yards away. He's half way up the pole and it's taken from his left rear quarter. No facial at all. Mom however, is another book entirely.

I only ever knew her as a laborer and a mother. She was born in Walla Walla, Washington on July 24, 1916. Given the name Lillian Jessup. Married first at 16 and eventually four or five times. At least three of her husbands, including Leroy, my father Jim, the father of my older half-brother and sister, Jim and Jorene, and a guy named Glenn, not to mention Pete ("the love of my life"), who perished in an airplane wreck, were Alaskan relationships. She lived in Alaska at least ten years between 1932 and 1949. During that time she flew Alaska like few do today. Nome to Ketchikan, Adak to Fairbanks—she would've been the first licensed lady bush pilot in Alaska had she continued that endeavor. Bill Egan, a three-term governor of the state, and she used to fly together when he was just out of California law school. She was also a "dime-a-dance-gal" at the Red Dog Saloon in the '30s. If nothing else, Mom knew how to have fun, seriously.

Within six months of arriving in Seattle with me she was pregnant with my other half-sister Judy. Mom told me she always wanted a brown eyed girl, so she married my step dad, Artis Douglas Berry Alford. Born on August 8 in the early to mid-'20s to a beautiful Cherokee woman, that everybody loved, and a first or second generation European man. He was one of nine or twelve kids. He adopted me when he married mom and they changed my name to his, complete with a Jr. on the end. I went to court in 1988 and dropped all the other names but Artis, since I wasn't relative to any of those folks. Ironically, he passed later that year, while I was in Australia performing at Expo '88. I was on very good terms with Dad, but hadn't seen him since my 20th birthday in 1968, when he gave me $40 and waited two hours till I got a ride, hitchhiking out of Florence, South Carolina, heading back to Patty, my daughter's mother, in Seattle. Mom and Dad were together 11 years. Definitely her longest marital relationship. He was a career Navy man. I was even stationed with him twice while I was in the Navy between 1965 and 1968. He wasn't around much when I was growing up. I remember when he was, there'd be folks around, young couples and single sailors, occasionally playing honky-tonk guitar and singing and drinking. He was handy with wood. He'd make bullroars, wooden boats (I remember an aircraft carrier he made), and sling shots he'd use to shoot pigeons off the roof. What a drag that was. I wasn't very surprised when Mom told me he wasn't my father, but only Judy's.

Mom always sang us to sleep with old swing era tunes like *Always, I'm Forever Blowing Bubbles, It's a Sin To Tell a Lie, Button Up Your Overcoat,* and her favorite, *Pennies From Heaven.* She'd also soft-shoe when she was havin' a good time. I learned to dance by standing on her feet and moving to the songs sung on the Perry Como Show, Lawrence Welk, Dick Clark and a show called the Hit Parade.

All I've ever aspired to do was sing. I started collecting records in 1956 or so. For more than ten years I bought only Elvis. I vowed to myself not to buy anybody else's unless I had all that Elvis had out at the time. That lasted until 1968 when there was no longer anyway to avoid the fact that Elvis was only one of many and not so exceptionally talented after all, especially as a writer or commentator. That field was being influenced now by Bob Dylan, the Beatles, P.F. Sloane (he wrote *Eve of Destruction),* Yoko Ono (even though none of us knew) and eventually Janis Joplin, Joan Baez, Pete Townsend and many, many more. The '60s.

The '60s to me were adolescence. Great changes in all my life and ways. The World's Fair to presidential assassination. Going from reasonable middle class security to penniless poverty in one year. Intelligent enough to drop out of high school and simultaneously dumb enough to join the military. LSD. Rock concerts. The Sky River Rock Festival. Hitchhiking across the nation and back, barefoot. Eventually in 1969 marrying Patty and on January 6, 1970, the birth of my daughter Roberta Love Lillian.

The '70s. Vital, developmental and innovative. Over two years at the post office. Buying a house, but not for long. The Satsop Rock Festival of 1973 marking the end of an era of multicultural outdoor "rock festivals." What had begun as commercial, cultural, casual events, presented for the sake of gathering, ended in a mudbath of untuned sounds, untamed drugs, unsure time-travellers and a watermelon truck driving through a tent encampment. But there was also the Oregon Country Fair, where I started performing. The Flying Karamazov Family, from whom I learned the true meaning of community. And

Joan, who taught me that loving one's self is more important than professing to love others. Naomi and Sari, my two step-daughters, were born in 1973 and 1977 respectively.

I began writing in the '70s. My first song was *1, 2, 3 Pretending to be Me*. I was sitting in a cafe at the Pike Place Market in Seattle called The Soup & Salad Cafe. I was seated next to a three step staircase while a young girl about three or four years old, was playing with a balloon. She would stand on a step, throw the balloon up in the air and run down the stairs to catch it saying "I'll catch it before it falls in the sea." My daughter was about her age at the time. I was enthralled with fatherdom and childish enchantment and still am. I wrote *Happy Ranch* in the same era, after a very enlightening and humbling visit to my friends in the Idaho woods. I wrote the song to express my gratitude.

My mother passed away in 1978. She passed 20 years to the week after her mother, at the same age and in the same manner. My grandmother, Edith, born in January or February of 1896, succumbed to a heart attack on December 14, 1958, after chasing Judy and me around the kitchen one night for getting into whatever she was cooking. Mom passed on December 18, 1978 from a stroke at home while she and her sweetie, Luke, were watching television. Five years later I retrieved my mother's ashes from the funeral home and the following year in early 1985, Joan and I buried them next to her mother's gravesite in Seattle. The song *Biodegradation* is inspired by that incident. The ashes were in a hard plastic box about the consistency of boom box plastic and the size of a large cigar box. It was wrapped in a pleasant grey mottled paper. Half the box was filled with styrofoam packing peanuts. The ashes were in a very heavy guage zip lock plastic baggie. How in the world, and I mean that literally, would anyone expect those ashes to ever get back to Earth, the source, if not the sustaining factor of all organisms that we are, as yet, aware of?

In the '80s I began to recognize my aspirations were manifesting. At age six or seven or even earlier I aspired to be an entertainer. In the '80s I was doing it full time—it had become a lifestyle. In the '50s I wanted to travel. In the '80s I went to 20 countries and all 50 U.S. states. In the '70s I dreamt of performing with Frank Zappa. In the '80s I did.

"The Spoonman" went through a course of casual refinement that no instructor could have designed, with camaraderie and guidance no guru could assign. Not the least of which were the "Band of Buzzards."

The Buzzards were Cowboy Dawg, Scarecrow the Insignificant, Master Gadget Master (MGM), the Wizard (of the ship of fools), Space Bass and myself. We came and went in a three year whirlwind from Seattle to Quartzite, from Mardi Gras to Bumbershoot, performing at campuses, street faires, festivals and on sidewalks wherever we went.

Tom Noddy (the Bubble Man) introduced me to television gigs in England and Japan that began my international excursions.

Joan, the most significant person in my adult life, deserves a whole book and much more. She opened my eyes to art.

I met Jim Page in 1971. He has been the strongest personal influence on my performing career and in 1989 we began a professional partnership.

My two stepsons, Philip and Kirk, and two of my three grandchildren were born in the '80s.

Ah, to abandon chronology and rigid form. . .someday.

Aspirations to Manifestations, from the Womb to the Void is a way of saying "dreams come true."

Spoon Playing in a Musical Sense

MY FIRST spoons at age ten were "musical spoons" purchased in a toy store for a few dollars. They are still available in some well-stocked music stores. They consist of two matched spoons held together at the handle by molded plastic. They were designed and manufactured by Walt Haines and produced by Lawrence Welk.

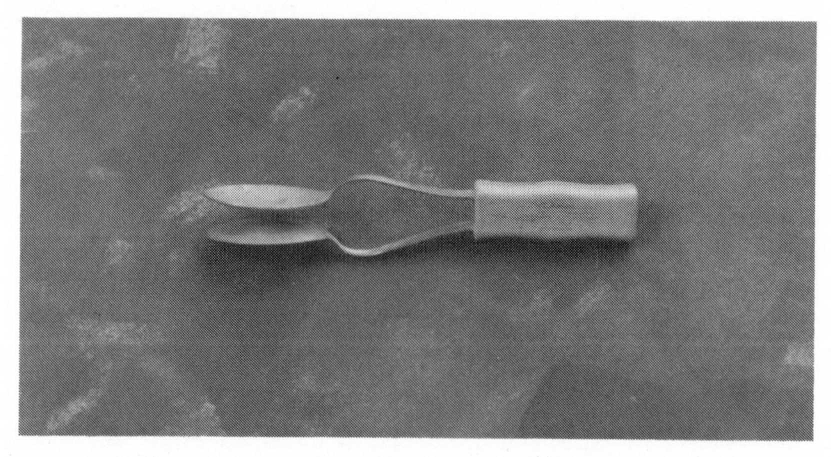

Another cheaper and equally effective way to acquire such a pair of spoons is to use a small block of wood, just big enough to hold between spoon handles and still keep the bowls of the spoons from touching when arranged bottom to bottom, as illustrated here. Wrap these two handles and block of wood fast together with elastic bands or tape. Voilà! Musical spoons.

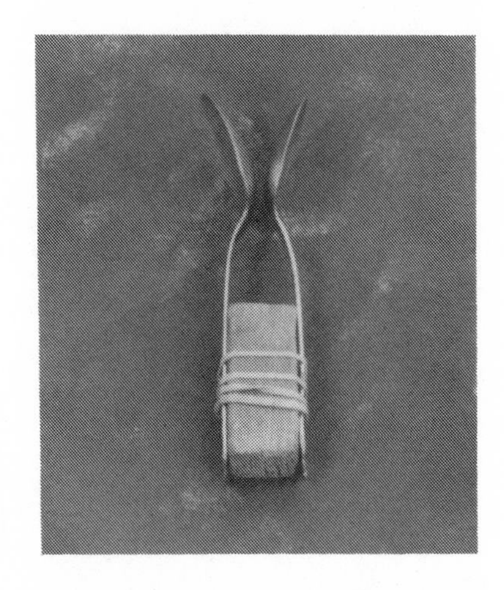

You may, of course, hold them without an incorporated handle; just two spoons gripped in your hand. There are innumerable ways to do this. I personally suggest you accept that, since you already have the inclination to check it out, and hold them any way that is most comfortable for you. That is, in fact, how I've done it. No one ever showed me how to hold them. I knew it could be done, so I just held them quite comfortably. As for blisters, callouses, slipping out of your hands while playing, etc., these all happen and will. C'est la vie!

This is the way I hold them and two other ideas I know of to be popular. I hold them two fingers apart, firmly, so that the bowls of the spoons are bottom to bottom, close but not touching. One spoon, "top" if you will, I hold between my thumb and first finger and the other spoon "bottom" I hold between my third and fourth finger. Again, my grip is firm and controlling. My hand is closed, but not like a fist. If you form with your hand the classic pretend gun, thumb up, forefinger pointed out and other three fingers closed, but back of hand relatively flat, then fold in your forefinger and drop your thumb—that's the basic form of my hand when holding two spoons.

You may hold the spoons one finger apart instead of two, or you might hold them on both sides of the thumb while the thumb is folded into the palm, and wrap the four fingers around the spoon handles and thumb. In this form the spoons protrude from the thumb end, not the little finger end.

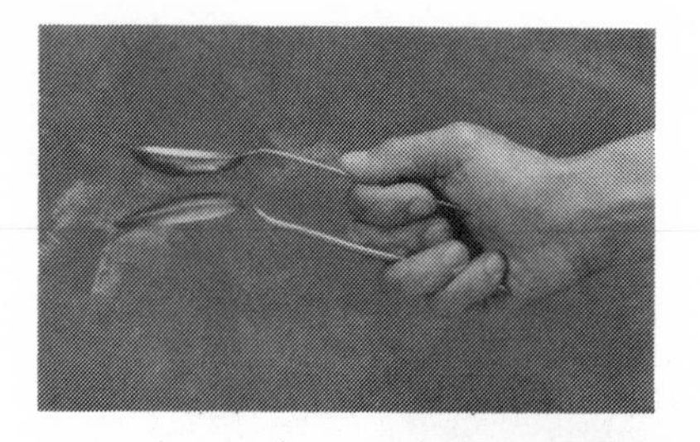

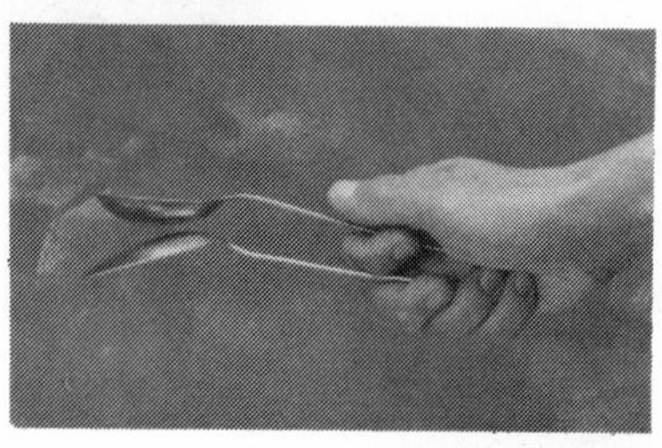

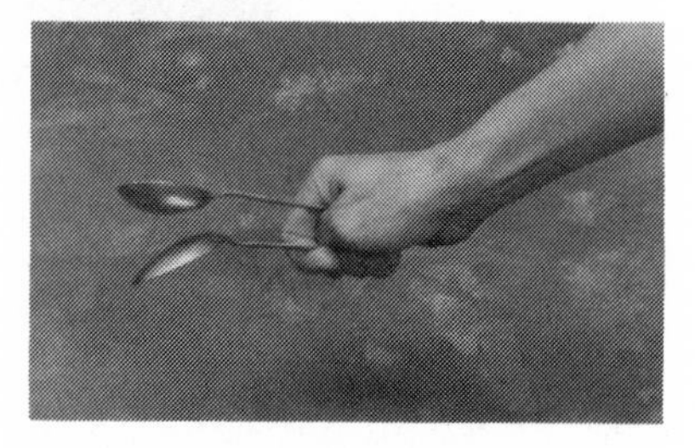

Strokes

I only do a few things, all of which are basic and simple—well, one may be a bit difficult, but difficulties are conceptual. If you're doing what you like, difficulties are no problem.

Briefly, play by hitting the spoons between your other hand and either leg. One beat down, one beat up, two beats down, one beat up, two beats up, one beat down—any combination you can relate to.

Run the spoons gently down the center of the *widespread* fingers of your other hand.

Run the spoons down your palm and biceps of your other arm onto one and then the other thigh.

Gently tap the spoons at your mouth where your cheek meets your mouth, half over your cheek, half over the cavity of your mouth, changing the tone by opening and closing your mouth ever so slightly.

Use any combination of these strokes in any pattern. Reverse them, change them, make up others, etc.

A nice and surprising effect is to lay two or more differently shaped and sounding spoons on some foam rubber and tap them with another spoon or stick as you would a drum. The sounds are far more brilliant than you might imagine. You get the same effect on blankets, soft furniture, grass lawn or carpeting.

All of these previously mentioned and described methods I learned from people's suggestions or the package my first "musical spoons" came in. The only thing I've developed on my own is how I grip them and two other methods of playing:

• Playing free-handed with the grip loosened just enough and wrist action appropriate to make the spoons I'm holding hit each other without also hitting another contact point—leg, hand, mouth, etc.

• Playing melodically, using the cup of the palm of my hand in conjunction with the "bottom" spoon, opening and closing my palm as I hit the spoon with the "top" spoon, varying the tonal pitch.

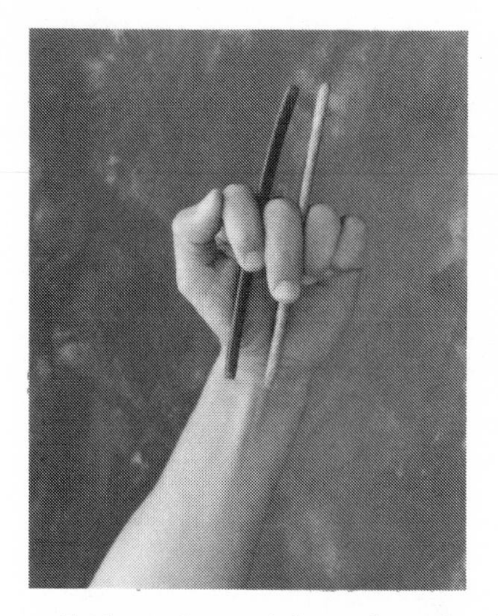

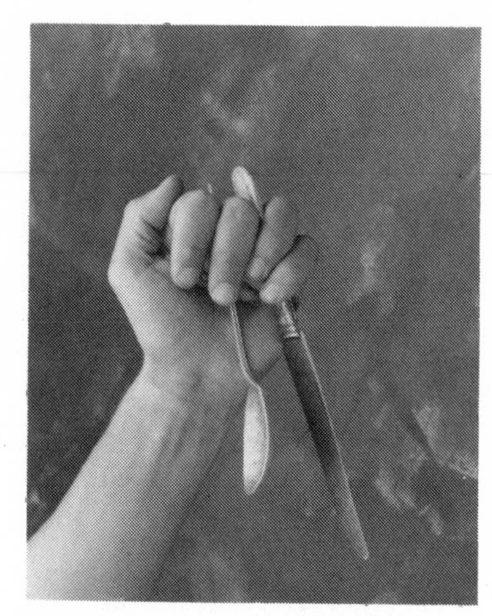

I also play sticks, after the fashion of "bones." Being of a vegetarian persuasion I only use animal products if absolutely necessary. Sticks, spoons, knives and even forks can all be played in the fashion of bones.

I place these instruments one on either side of my middle finger, gripping firmly to the palm of my hand curve to curve, bowl to bowl, with one end extended further towards the wrist or with straight sticks, in the center of the sticks, equal amounts extending inside and outside my grip.

You grip sticks firmly; however, the one on the little finger side is the one that is loosened enough to rock. With this grip simply cock your wrist back and bend your elbow and wave. *Literally* wave. Use your other hand and wave to a friend or imagined friend and simulate the *same* action with the sticks. Don't loosen your grip on the thumbward stick, and loosen it only slightly on the other. Keep this in mind: your hand and arm waving creates a la-la, la-la, 1-2, 1-2 rhythm while when the sticks get it they create a diddledi, diddledi, 1-2-3, 1-2-3 rhythm. Not directly correlative, so just wave. It'll come. You'll hear it. When it gets frustrating, get mad at it and try harder—it's only a toy of your own expressions.

In closing I'd like to say if you have more questions don't ever hesitate to ask me. The bottom line of my abilities, however, is my own eccentric involvement and the belief that there

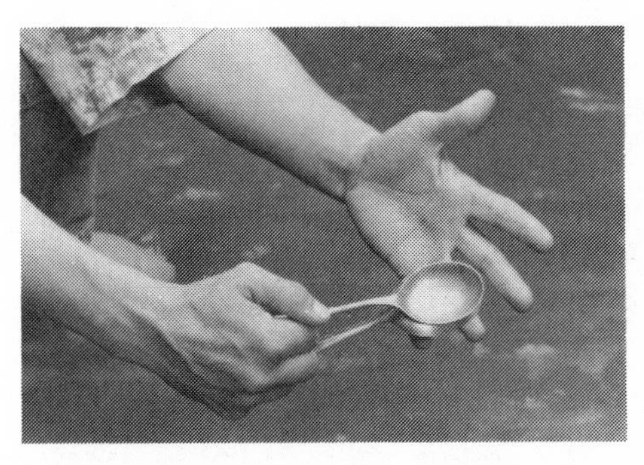

are no secondary instruments, only attitudes that place objects in other than primary positions. You may play spoons, tap table tops, whistle, or quietly concentrate on a rhythm and find all the satisfaction of a concert pianist or any member of any conventional orchestration. If you have a heartbeat, you have rhythm. You may not play to another's beat, more power to you. You may not exploit it, however graciously, as I do and other "professional" musicians. You still have rhythm and your involvement is essential and primary and represents harmony.

P.S. If the clackity-clack is too much for your housemates, put tape on the "bottom" of the spoons. This also makes metal spoons sound a bit like wooden spoons, while acting as a formidable mute. Cheers!

Busking

BUSKING: a word that may be rooted in old English, meaning *business* of the *king*. Today, however, as I define it and find it commonly, it is an English word for the art of entertainment, indoors or out, with receptacle for donations, anywhere, anytime, on or about all human domains. Entertainment for *everybody*, not a select, elite few who are the "right" color of skin, the "right" religion, sex, or age, or have the "right" amount of cash to afford the show. It is entertainment with no cover charge, minimum drink or drug oriented atmosphere, dress code or mediator (mob, syndicate, or "boss") controlling the material being offered.

I'm quite sure it's the original form of entertainment. It's a respectable, honourable, and admirable profession, not to be confused with begging, panhandling, or bumming. It is not "something for nothing." It's entertainment for *fair* exchange; the audience determines freely what's fair.

In my own words, as I understand it and feel it, that's busking.

I believe the highest compliment one can bestow upon another is attention. Picture this: you're walking from point A to point B, either with a predetermined destination or at leisure with no particular plan. Along the way you are distracted by a performance just a few feet out of your way. You stop. You linger. You enjoy it. You support it with any number of appreciative expressions. For example, applause, monetary contribution, remarking to others of what you've witnessed, remarking to the performer(s) your thoughts on what you witnessed, etc.

Is there a *more* vital form of social intercourse?

My personal experiences with busking have found me playing for hours for a dollar and a dime (two tips)—the dime from an insulting young white male student and the dollar from a middle-aged Asian woman who ran after me down the street to give it to me—to receiving as much as 200 U.S. dollars in one hat pass and a100 dollar bill tip four different times in my career so far.

It has found me arrested and charged with "inciting a mob." (When the officer arrived to tell me we were playing on the wrong side of the sidewalk, there were maybe ten or 12 people watching. When the car drove me away as prisoner, maybe one hundred people had gathered to watch, still an audience, not a mob, and formed to witness an arrest, not a performance.) Damn! 12 people immediately followed to the precinct and complained, I was released, and when I showed in court, charges were dropped.

It has also found me undeservingly celebrated by many people, of all ages, for well over a decade. I say "undeservingly" because if the truth be known, as a solo performer, I dread, unto the point of hatred, busking. I have never enjoyed the prospect of busking alone. I have to stoop to play and I am so eccentrically involved, I feel people look upon me as a bum and a freak with little or no redeeming qualities, an aimless fool.

My attachment to music is the most satisfying and dependably uplifting relationship I have with my perception of myself and the material plane of living. To perform in any healthy setting, with any competent musicians, doesn't bother me a bit, but my ego and false sense of insecurity about such mundane things as social acceptance and personal image have kept me quite ill physically and emotionally over busking alone.

In closing, I have no criticisms to make of any audiences, anywhere, but as for laws outlawing busking I say *BUNK!!* Entertainment is a vital and valuable asset to all communities. No tribe or society has ever existed without it. It does not need to be bought up and sold back to us by syndicates and corporations and governments under the rubric "popular." Sound levels can be regulated by decibel count, equally adhered to by passing vehicles, industry and instruments of music. When space is limited and being compromised, performers should accept the responsibility of finding appropriate locations. As for disturbance, if a performance is not attended or supported it will eventually fade. If the performance grows in popularity then the responsibility of any "disturbance" lies equally with performers and audience. In a "democracy," compromises, gains and losses are equally shared by *all* parties to find a harmonious medium not dominated with power for the sake of the few *or* the many.

Peace.

Then

IT HAS BEEN two, maybe three thousand years since Humanity has written, with any serious intent. The last serious writing, that I know of, was *Absolute Life on Earth,* by the combined wisdom of the planet Earth. It was presented to the public in the year 2948. Of course, there was only one writing. Copies were distributed throughout the planet, and to all known universal aliens. Other than *THE BOOK,* I suppose, a few writings were published, but not many.

Writing dates back quite a few thousand years, as you know. It became the only universally accepted communication bridge, and remained that way until Humanity found electricity. Once electricity was put to use it took less than 1,000 years to eliminate the usefulness of writing.

The telegraph, to the best of my knowledge, was first to replace writing. Then came radio, television, tape recordings, cinerama, stereovision, hologram, TruVu, MindVu and a few other experiments. Until the year 3006, no other communications were totally accepted. Then telepathy finally took over.

Telepathy, would you believe, has been struggling since the beginning, and has only been in power for 2,000 years? Humanity was the only being that refused to believe in it. Every other being on Earth, Venus, Mars, Saturn and Galaxiou used it totally. Not Humanity! Humanity used it approximately 10 to 15 percent of the time. It is still a mystery as to why. Humanity has evolved 85 percent in the last 2,000 years, compared to the 15 percent from "the beginning" to the year 3000.

I won't bore you with what you already know. Please,

forgive me. I am writing this just to satisfy my dying limb. Yes! I am a mutant. Perhaps the last on this planet. You would certainly think me ugly if you saw me. I have a full arm and hand and four fingers (I cut one off) protruding from my home. It's monstrous too. In length it makes two average homes, but only one-third as thick. It's exactly 30 inches long, from home to fingertip. It is 105 years old now. It should die anytime. I would've killed it years ago, but the pain would have killed me. I found out when I cut off the finger. The pain nearly killed me. I went into a coma for ten years.

I realize few of you have ever experienced pain, so you're naturally curious. Let me tell you, it's the DEVIL. Due to our homes, we (that is, humanoid man) never experience pain. Our cells are perfectly protected by our epidermis homes. But if you happen to be a mutant you cannot protect your "body." The "body" has a skin of its own, unlike that of the brain. It resists any limiting shelter. It must move, it has muscles. The brain, of course, has no muscles, and since the skull has evolved to a thin shell, our "epidermis" homes are perfect shelter.

Being a mutant is very difficult. Your "body" can bring about your death if you don't take absolute care. The brain can keep itself alive even after the "body's" death, as you know, but if the "body" is not perfectly disposed of, poison can spread. So, if you are a mutant you must keep your "body" alive until it dies naturally.

That brings me to the reason I'm writing. After 105 years I have become "attached" to my arm. I have exercised it continuously except for my ten year sleep. It hurt so bad that I had to exercise to keep from going into another coma. I have done many strange things. I have crawled, swung, jumped, made noise, I even broke something once. But I have never written. It's interesting, but extremely trying. Nobody will ever read it. It will only be absorbed telepathically by Humanity, and no known aliens read.

Oh well! Soon my arm will die and I will be able to live a normal life. Strange though! I think I'll miss it.

My name is unnecessary for you to know. Someday soon I will be just like you. I have written this in all known languages and equations. It has taken me 26 days and nights to record this. I have used an old diamond rod I found in my wanderings. This is written in an area measuring 0.8737 acre, in a location I will not disclose at this time.

I have contributed the sum of this thought to the BANK for absolute preservation. I have communicated this throughout my telepathic range. Having come this far I am satisfied to make this the last word.

Wiley and the Sparkle Tree

AS HARD as this is to believe, there is a tree, right in the middle of a forest, that is quite possibly the most unusual tree in the world. And, even more difficult as it may be to believe, this same tree is located in the exact center of every forest in every country in the world except Ireland. And this is the story of one such tree and one special individual named Wiley.

Now, the tree is quite tall, as tall as the tallest trees right nearby. Its trunk is rather large, with a bit of a green/brown hue to it. And all about the upper part of the tree is the most fragile looking greenery your eyes have ever beheld. It has the appearance of fine green lace (a bit like asparagus fern), ranging from about a third of the way up the trunk (which by the way is not unlike a redwood trunk) all the way to the top and out for several meters in all directions. The most glorious thing of this tree is that whether day or night it appears to sparkle. Now, we know that it's only the light and the way it hits the tree, but I swear to you that when you're in its presence, it'll seem to sparkle of its own accord.

There came an evening, not too long ago, when a quiet little leprechaun by the name of Wiley was strolling through this forest, which happened to be, by the by, located on a little known area within the bounds of the country of Albania, when he found himself standing smack dab in front of the sparkle tree. Wiley, being somewhere between three and four hundred years old, was not exceptionally impressed, having seen a lot in his lifetime. However, he did marvel at the beauty of this very

unique tree. Tired and weary as he was, he sat and gazed upon it for awhile.

You must remember, leprechauns are a bit small, seldom reaching more than six inches in height, as I understand, and Wiley being a bit old and tired was not the tallest of leprechauns. So, in his eyes this tree was big enough to fill his whole view when he got close enough and that's when he noticed the marvel of the trunk. For the trunk seemed to be carved like an intricate wood block. Wiley would have considered it the work of worms had he not noticed that some of the apparent carvings came right down to his feet where he stood, at the roots of the tree. "Blimey!" thought Wiley, "this looks like a bit of a pathway carved right into the tree, and it's certainly big enough for my little feet. Perhaps I should venture a little further." And venture he did.

As he gazed ahead at the trunk of the tree, it seemed to be carved with scenes of villages, pathways, farms and houses. "Well, now this is a marvelous tree," Wiley said out loud, half hoping someone might hear, reflecting on his several years of solitude now, but not remorsefully. He walked a bit farther and before he knew it, he was surrounded with hills, rockery, paths and roadways, and much to his amazement, although he knew he was walking straight up a tree it felt, looked and seemed as if he was walking on solid ground. He wondered for a brief moment as he strolled, "Could this be a spell brought on by that little prankster Liam? Why, I bet I haven't seen him in a stone's age. But no matter, it's a pleasant experience, shouldn't trouble myself with worry."

So on he walked and it wasn't very long before he saw a road lead off to the left, so he took it, feeling a bit familiar with the surroundings. And a few steps further, he found himself crossing a bridge, and just ahead, a hill with houses. Wiley had no sooner crossed the bridge when he stopped short and exclaimed, "Krikey! This must be a spell! I just walked over a bridge with a river of water flowing under it!! And look at this place. It reminds me of Killorglin. Well, bowl me over like a ninepin. It not only reminds me of Killorglin but it feels like it and it looks like it. I best be resting my weary noggin." And with that, he leaned against the bridge post with wonder for just a moment. Not being one to ponder the whys and ways of nature or spells for that matter, unless of course they turn for the worst, he decided to stroll on up the hill.

It wasn't until Wiley was at the top of the hill that he came to the sudden realization that he was not the only moving creature about. Fortunately for him he did realize, and just in the nick of time, for it appeared this must be a Sunday as there were cattle in the street (Sunday being cattle market day in Killorglin), and people milling about. Wiley came just a hair's breadth from being smashed into oblivion by the hoof of a rather rambunctious bull. Since he did come to his senses, it gave him an opportunity to exercise some of his valuable leprechaun talent, as this bull in his anxiety had leaned against a storefront window, right up to and in fact surpassing the window's breaking point. Wiley immediately cast his gaze to the window, knowing quite well it was about to break (and the bull would not pay for it), twitched his fingers and uttered the words of an ageless mystic spell, which I am afraid I cannot reveal—sorry, a secret, you know; wouldn't want it misused. Sure as you're born, the window remained intact and no one ever knew the difference. Shhhhh! Except you and me, of course.

Well, Wiley was beside himself as you might well imagine, but as I've said before, not being one to ponder the wonders of nature or the mystery of spells unless of course they're adverse, Wiley quickly hobbled down the nearest road and out of town, completely unnoticed, as usual, by all save a few insects and fairies. It wasn't long before he was well out of town and surrounded solely by small rolling hills, green grass, small roadways and miles and miles of rock walls. That's when he decided he would ponder this magical mystery (tour?). So, he leaned himself up against a particularly comfortable looking rock wall and slowly and methodically began to recount the 370 years of his life in hopes of finding the answer to this riddle.

Now as you might imagine, 370 years is a long time and to recount one's wisdoms and adventures over such a period would take perhaps an equally long time, and that's just what Wiley did. And it wasn't until he had recounted all the way back to some of his very earliest years that he remembered an old leprechaun adage spoken to him by the oldest leprechaun he had ever known, his most distant grandfather, Brendon O'Flaherty, who said to him, "Wiley, m'lad, old leprechauns never die, they just return to the land of Eire."

Dream Castle

For Quinn, June 1992

SOMEWHERE in the beautiful puffy clouds of dreamskies there's a dream castle for everybody. Each one is different, but they all serve the same purpose; to house the tools, toys, incentive and courage to plan and design one's own life while resting in deep sleep. A place to play freely and abstractly, testing the creativity one will use while awake later on.

This is a story of one such castle and one dreamer, and one dream-maker.

This dream castle had a special difference. It could only be reached while in deep sleep on a freshly mown haystack.

There once was a kind farmer who was so fond of music and children and all the sounds of nature that he would occasionally venture to the city and seek out children to play music to. He'd go to the schools, parks, streets and playgrounds. He'd play flutes, sticks, hand drums, whistles, spoons, even stones, and sing and tell stories. Not all at once, of course. He'd always share his instruments and teach how he played and how to make other musical instruments out of clay, or oil cans, or bottles, or water hoses, or seaweed or bamboo, and how to play your own body by clapping hands, and singing, and whistling and tapping feet and dancing. The main thing he taught, though, was harmony, sharing, playing together and listening.

Sometimes he would arrange with schools and parents to take the children to the country. They wouldn't take instruments to the country. The farmer would instead draw their attention to the sounds and rhythms in the atmosphere all about them. They'd listen to the water in brooks babbling like rocks lightly popping and in rivers rushing like a great roar. They'd listen to the water after a rain dropping from trees and try to pick out a rhythm. They'd listen to the birds chirping and pecking and screeching and cooing and flapping their wings. They'd hear the leaves rustle in the breeze, the insects buzzing and whirring. Even the quiet and stillness had a rhythm and sound of its own.

One day a little friend of the musical farmer decided to go to the country and visit, since it had been so long since she had seen him.

She prepared for a long day. She left early and carried water and a snack. Along the way she'd sing songs the musical farmer had inspired her to create, and while she sang, birds would chirp and she'd chirp back and stop for a moment or two. Then a while later while whistling and walking she'd hear the water in a nearby stream and whistle a tune to the rhythm of the water. She'd go a bit farther and the breeze would blow through the trees coaxing her to dance, and she'd twirl and prance and lightly leap to the sounds.

Eventually she became a bit tired and noticed a field with dozens of haystacks scattered all about it. A little farther up the road she could see the musical farmer's house. So, she decided to sit and drink some water and have a snack before she continued.

She found a nice fluffy haystack and fell onto it with glee. She lay back and closed her eyes to rest for a moment and before you could count to your favorite number she was fast asleep, and while she slept she paid a wonderful visit to the dream castle, where she played and planned, designed and created, freely and abstractly, her life.

Sleep well in your dream castle, little friend.

Be Yourself, Nobody Else Can

1, 2, 3 PRETENDING TO BE ME

1, 2, 3 I'll let this bubble free
& I'll bet you I can catch it
'fore it falls into the sea

I'm standing on some stairs
there must be 3 or 4
& the sea that I imagine
well, of course, it is the floor

1, 2, 3 I'll let this bubble free
& I'll bet you I can catch it
'fore it falls into the sea

Surely you must think
that I'm as silly as a loon
the bubble I am tossing
is just a red balloon

1, 2, 3 I'll let this bubble free
& I'll bet you I can catch it
'fore it falls into the sea

You see I'm just a little tyke
pretending to be me

but if it's something else you like
your patience is the fee

1, 2, 3 I'll let this bubble free
& I'll bet you I can catch it
'for it falls into the sea

1974

HAPPY RANCH

If you'll forgive my boldness
I've got something to say
I've been 3 weeks in the wilderness
with a family by the way
Happy Ranch we call it
& Happy it should be
the work is never ending
but the pace is patient—Lee

These people have accepted me
for much more than I'm worth
& they send me with a feeling
to take care of precious earth

So here I am a-wandering along my destined way
knowing I could've 'ever stayed another day
I say this in this manner
cuz I know no other way
to thank these people & to carry on
such a warm & pleasant stay.

1975

PIKE PLACE MARKET

The Pike Place Market
Pike place mall to be
This sterile renovation
makes no good sense to me

The poor set the trends
for the need to progress
while the rich buy it up
always leaving them with less

The Pike Place Market
Pike place mall to be
This sterile renovation
makes no good sense to me

Working people built it
so many years ago
Now the power's saying
the poor will have to go

The Pike Place Market
Pike place mall to be
This sterile renovation
makes no good sense to me

If you people want a mall
there's one in every town
There's not a Pike Place Market
anywhere else around

The Pike Place Market
Pike place mall to be
This sterile renovation
makes no good sense to me

1976

TOAD FISH

It's a toad fish, it's a toad fish
moving right along
It's a toad fish, it's a toad fish
cruising right along

It's got 4 round legs and a whole lot of glass
it's just a big steel box,
always wanting to pass

It's a toad fish, it's a toad fish
moving right along
It's a toad fish, it's a toad fish
cruising right along

It's got 2 beady eyes staring out from the left
& sometimes there's two on the right
It's got 2 big eyes glaring out from the front
& if it hits you, you better hope it's a bump

cuz it's a toad fish, it's a toad fish
moving right along
It's a toad fish, it's a toad fish
cruising right along

It thrives on a diet of petroleum
you know it sucks it up like a kid on a thumb
Its home is a river of tar & cement
& when it dies there's no one around to lament

It's a toad fish, it's a toad fish
moving right along
It's a toad fish, it's a toad fish
cruising right along

Now there's a dichotomy attached to my rhyme
It's simply, I'd like to have a toad fish of mine
It don't need to go fast or run on no gas.

1975

ALL AM ARE

All am are, All am are
The seas, the trees, the skies, the flies
the teepees, the domes, the condominium homes

ALL AM ARE

The children, the grown ups
the stuff we've all thrown up
the colours, the lines,
the good and bad times

ALL AM ARE

The sun, the pain
the fun, the rain
the black holes in space
the things we can't trace

ALL AM ARE

This song came to me
so I give it to you
Please give it to somebody else when you're through

ALL AM ARE

1976

LIFE

I don't know what life's all about
but I'm love, love, love livin' to find out
I don't know what life's all about
but I'm love, love, love livin' to find out

I've never lived in a war zone
I've never really been alone
only had one broken bone
but I know my tone is our own

I don't know what life's all about
but I'm love, love, love livin' to find out
I don't know what life's all about
but I'm love, love, love livin' to find out

My feelings of growth
often leave me with doubt
sometimes I feel like a seed that can't sprout
I wanna sing out
I wanna sing out
I wanna sing out

I don't know what life's all about
but I'm love, love, love livin' to find out
I don't know what life's all about
but I'm love, love, love livin' to find out

Music, love & romance
give you reason to dance
Get up off your pants
It might be your last chance

I don't know what life's all about
but I'm love, love, love livin' to find out
I don't know what life's all about
but I'm love, love, love livin' to find out

1977

DOLLAR BILL

I dropped a dollar bill on the sidewalk,
hoping someone poor might find it
"Good luck"
as I kicked it good-bye

Looking around me, under the starlit sky
I noticed 2 people a block or so away

who looked to me to be in quite sufficient pay
  "I hope they don't see it,
  I hope they don't see it"

As I strolled on along, I looked back to see
the woman bending over where the dollar would be
"Isn't it fun to find money?" I said
as they soon passed me by
She said "Oh! You saw it too?"
I said "I dropped it"
She said "So did I," she said "So did I,
we don't need it, felt guilty to keep it,
so we just passed it by"
  So she just passed it by
Maybe you found it & had breakfast the next day.
I just mean to say
That all money's not pay.
 True Story

1977

REAL STORY

When he was 8 years old
he built his own go kart
when he was 12
he designed an airplane
when he was 16
he built his own flying disc
  The anxiety of his secrecy
  caused him pain
he'd take it to the desert sometimes
to fly it around
up to 500 feet, then skimming along the ground

"Field unit 3 to command,
we have UFO under surveillance at 60 yards
it is motionless & we have it surrounded"

"MAJOR! MAJOR! There's something coming out"

"ALL ARMS READY! FIRE!!"

". . .on the lighter side of the news tonight
the air force has determined last night's UFO sighting
as a radio- or light-wave phenomenon.
Not entirely uncommon to this vicinity
but definitely not a vehicle from another planet or
galaxy."

When he was 8 years old
he built his own go kart
when he was 12
he designed an airplane
when he was 16 years old
he left home & was never heard from again.

1978

MY BAND

I really love to sing
sing out as good as I can
harmonize with others
but who wants to be in my band?

My sex life ain't none of your business
& yours sure ain't none of mine
& I don't want to sing about it
not even if the story do rhyme

I don't need no mind pluckin' intoxicants
coffee, dope or drink
It's hard enough to stay sober
with the thoughts one has to think.

I really love to sing
sing out as good as I can
harmonize with others
but who wants to be in my band?

You know where you can stick
your negative/positive jive
I know by God I'm being here
& I'm glad to be alive

I don't know enough about God to tell
don't believe all that I've read
but control by police & politics
are for those who still need to be led

I really love to sing
sing out as good as I can
harmonize with others
but who wants to be in my band?
I really love to sing
sing out as hard as I can
but what is there to sing about
& who wants to be in my band?

1981

I'M A FOOL

I'm a fool, I'm a fool,
I'm a foo-oo-oo-ool, I'm a fool

I don't want to struggle or strife
I just want to play my life
don't want to argue, wrong or right
bound to run away from any fight
but

I'm a fool, I'm a fool,
I'm a foo-oo-oo-ool, I'm a fool

I think about the year 2050
the newborn now will still be 60
I wonder if they'll still be alive
I wonder if their parents will survive
but that's us

I'm a fool, I'm a fool,
I'm a foo-oo-oo-ool, I'm a fool

I try to think in colours, music & rhyme
don't worry 'bout all the things that are mine
I know that a patriot is true to the world
& no one country is the ultimate pearl
& when I'm angry I know that I'm wrong
The ultimate solution will be sung in a song
The ultimate solution will be sung in a song
The ultimate solution will be sung
but

I'm a fool, I'm a fool,
I'm a foo-oo-oo-ool, I'm a fool

1982

NO HITCH HIKING

I will ride in the back if I can friend
I will ride in the back if I can
If you're going somewhere
& you've got room to spare
I will ride in the back if I can

No hitch hiking, don't you go the freeway
No hitch hiking, if you gonna ride

you gotta pay
If you gonna ride, you gotta pay
Well I cruise down the road in the mutual mode
giving rides, gettin' rides as I go
while the media screams, with its paranoid themes
NO, NO, NO, NO, NO, NO, NO

No hitch hiking, don't you go the freeway
No hitch hiking, if you gonna ride
you gotta pay,
If you gonna ride, you gotta pay

Ole Ike said, "Build me some roads
that'll transport the convoys
at 90 miles an hour"
Well it took 30 years to put them under our wheels
but don't you think for 1 minute they're ours
(they can shut them down in just a matter of 4 hours)

No hitch hiking, don't you go the freeway
No hitch hiking, if you gonna ride
you gotta pay,
If you gonna ride, you gotta pay

I will ride in the back if I can friend
I will ride in the back if I can
If you're going somewhere
& you've got room to spare
I will ride in the back if I can
I will ride in the back of your
pick-up truck "Cadillac"
I will ride in the back if I can

1982

PROGRAM

Tune in to your favorite program
program, program
Entertainment, you say
I say Program, Program, Program
Entertainment is a natural resource, resource, resource
It's as valuable as air & water
If you haven't thought of this
you oughta, you oughta, they oughta

No tribe or society has ever existed without it
don't doubt it, think about it
live without it

Cuz it's illegal in most of these nations
to perform for free or accept donations
& where it's not illegal, it's considered less than equal
to that which is controlled by corporations
corporations, corporations, corporations
You've got Kissinger, Haig & former president Ford
all on the executive board of directors, directors, directors
of 20th Century Fox, MGM, & United Artists
ARTISTS? ARTISTS? ARTISTS?
With "Death Valley" Reagan as president
they call that entertainment
Entertainment you say? I say Program, Program, Program
Tune in to your favorite Program, Program, Program,
Program.

1982

LISTEN

I can talk to you about sex abuse & nuclear misuse
About organic gardening & nude sunbathing
& a multitude of topical issues
But can I talk to you about Punks?

about throwing up on a stage?
about the youth so sick that their hearts are enraged
Because the hippies of the 60's
with their flowers and peace
sat back on their ass
with their too precious grass
while the next generation were being overcome
by the wrong educational system

So, it's 20 years later, you still wanna hear
Garcia & Jagger & a little Blue Cheer eer eer
Well the wave's rollin' in & it ain't lookin' back
To watch peace jivin' pacifists lie on the tracks
The aggressive oppressors' been suckin' their brains
while their parents & friends been lyin' 'round lame
It's a wonder they don't feel just a little insane
They're screamin' in pain
with every refrain
LISTEN! LISTEN!!

1986

BOY BLUES

First thing in my life, they cut me with a knife
Took me straight from the womb
to the operating room
Made a covenant with him
Huh!!
cut away my foreskin—NOOOOO!!!

Don't say it doesn't hurt, you stupid little jerk
Stick a pin in your eye. NO! Don't you dare cry
I didn't make that decision, give me back my foreskin
Give me back my foreskin!!
Give me back my foreskin!!
Give me back my foreskin!!
Give me back my foreskin!!

& what about your own, don't you kinda wanna moan?
when you're suckling your wife
aren't you wondering why?
could it be you still hurt, from the pain at birth
& you wanna ask your mom
why she let 'em cut your schlong? NOOOOO!!!

I can keep myself clean like the girls all do
Don't tell me it's religion or that we're the precious few
The pain's still the same, I don't care what you claim

First thing in my life, they cut me with a knife
Took me straight from the womb
to the operating room
made a covenant with him
Huh!!
cut away my foreskin—NOOOOO!!

1986

INSTITUTE OF ROMANCE

The institute of romance is a fallacy
the honesty of love is reality
If you think that you're in love with what you see
it's gonna break your heart eventually
Romance can be used to enhance the time
when life seems slow, there's a row to hoe
it'll flat out ease your mind
Love cannot be seen, held or talked about
but it's been here forever without a doubt

So many couples today only last a few years
They think & hope that romance
will see them through the tears
But if they know each other
& the truth could all be heard

the anxiety of romance
all seems so absurd

Who am I to say all this?
Now don't you ask me that
cuz I am me, & you are you
& that's a natural fact
Our mothers were not virgins
& we're not saviours & that's excuse enough
for our behaviours

The institute of romance is a fallacy
the honesty of love is reality
If you think that you're in love with what you see
it's gonna break your heart eventually
Romance can be used to enhance the time
when life seems slow, there's a row to hoe
it'll flat out ease your mind
Love cannot be seen, held, or talked about
but it's been here forever without a doubt

The institute of romance is a fallacy
The honesty of Love is reality.

1987

LIFE'S A VACATION

I play for a livin'
I work for fun
Live for the joy of it
Life's a vacation

Life's a vacation!!
Life's a vacation!!

1987

Alien Retro-Transitting Inner Space

MR. AMERICA

Mr. America you're embarrassing me
in your attempt to be equal
you play superiority, to all the women you see

I never met a woman that wasn't stronger than me
in every way, proportionately
But because your penis was clipped
& you haven't got a womb
your equality suffers an imminent doom
well, accept it as fate & get on with your life
& don't take it out on our whole lovely wife/sister
MISTER
AMERICA

You're embarrassing me
I can't let you do it anymore, don't you see?
You're drafting all our brothers into phallocrat war
& treating all our sisters in a way I abhor
The ultra-perverted few at the top of the heap
are just as innocent as newborn babies in sleep
Still they continue to destroy all that's precious & pure
To end their ignorance is the only sure cure
So I'm telling them, like I'm telling you too

Mr. America you're embarrassing me
in your attempt to be equal
you play superiority, to all the women you see

I never met a woman that wasn't stronger than me
in every way, proportionately
But because your penis was clipped
& you haven't got a womb
your equality suffers an imminent doom
well, accept it as fate & get on with your life
& don't take it out on our whole lovely wife/sister
MISTER
AMERICA

Mr. Japan, Mr. Mediterranean, Mr. Australia, Mr. Canada
& on & on & on. . .I suggest you take her off the pedestal
& share the podium

1987

ECONOMIC STARDUST

Do you own it, or do you owe on it?
Do you own it, or does it own you?
Let's get down to the facts of it,
what about the tax on it?
Do you own it, or does it own you?

Is that your car, does it belong to the savings & loan?
Is that your house, or are you just calling it home?
Do you own those clothes, have you paid for them yet?
Face it friends, we're too far in debt.

Do you own it, or do you owe on it?
Do you own it, or does it own you?
Let's get down to the facts of it,
what about the tax on it?
Do you own it, or does it own you?

Borrow, lend, speculate,
it all breaks down to the interest rate
Is it trust, or lust for the equity
that entices us to live beyond our means
fulfilling someone else's dream
While they're vamping all our energy
do you thank the banks for your destiny?

Do you own it, or do you owe on it?
Do you own it, or does it own you?
Let's get down to the facts of it,
what about the tax on it?
Do you own it, or does it own you?

I was born unto my mother
not a church, state or a nation
& I will strive one way or another
to avoid a warring taxation
I won't subscribe to intimidation
by technological proliferation
without responsible dedication

Do you own it, or do you owe on it?
Do you own it, or does it own you?
Let's get down to the facts of it,
what about the tax on it?
Do you own it?

1990

FATHER TIME

to Thomas Logg, Fremont, 1972

Father Time is a Wizard
Father Time is a Wizard
He's got long white hair
He's got a long white beard

He stands 6 feet tall
He ain't got no teeth at all

Father Time is a Wizard

He don't try to make you feel glad
He don't try to make you feel sad
He don't try to make you feel good
He try to make you feel like you should

Father Time is a Wizard

He flies through the universe
stealing eggs from the CosmicGoose
only to return them again
just as soon as they're hatched

Father Time is a Wizard
Father Time is a Wizard
& he goes by the name of Tom

1975

BIO-DEGRADATION

When this body loses its identity
it'll stop breathin', its heart will stop pumpin'
its thought waves will no longer exist
But it'll still be alive
at the cellular level
so, please let it

Biodegrade at a natural rate
let the cells integrate so they can reincarnate
Don't mean to shake any tree of ideology
but my theology says
Please let me be free to

biodegrade at a natural rate
let the cells integrate so they can reincarnate

If I should disappear, don't you worry 'bout me
If I happen to drown, leave me there in the sea
you can reuse any worthy part of this body
& if you burn it, in my ashes, please plant a tree
I've got to—

Biodegrade at a natural rate
let the cells integrate so they can reincarnate

Don't want formaldehyde gel to pickle my cells
keepin' this body embalmed, in a state of uncalm
Don't let this body get locked inside a plastic box
with the earth all around, but no way to touch ground
I've got to—

Biodegrade at a natural rate
let the cells integrate so they can reincarnate
don't want to shake any tree of ideology
but my theology says
Please let me be free

1987

OCF—ESSENTIAL EVENT

Let's be detached about it
let the lightness remain
Don't take it personal
we don't need the pain
We're all here dedicated
to keeping things sane
If our friendship is on the line
there's nothing to gain

Essential event, essential event
Essential event, essential event
You can't take it home
to a mind that's never known
an experience that's quite like
this one
The space is so enchanted
The scope is so expanded
The imagery defies definition
Essential event, essential event
Essential event, essential event

But we can take the image
& project it through our thoughts
to the mind of someone
who can receive it
& even if it comes in dreams
& they think it's fantasy
they'll have an vision
they can carry it on with
We have an vision we can carry it on with
It's all an vision that's been carried on

Essential event, essential event
Essential event
This is an essential event
Essential event, essential event
Essential event
This is an essential event

1989

ETERNALLY NOW

My heart wants to leap out & sing YO!!
Let me beat out the rhythm of life
at a pace y'all can groove along with.
My ears want to hear & assimilate

every audible tone
to keep my heart in time with all.
Let my body transcend identity
& vibrate with knowledge & joy,
love, vitality & harmony.
Let my eyes see the atomic continuity in space
& celebrate the ultimate equality of it all.
Let my ego accept the responsibility
of properly directing its arrogance & pride
to benefit the community of egos at large.
Let my passion be as a thousand light years of life
squeezed into 150 earth years
with the accuracy of the quintessential marksmen
& Please, Please
let my voice cry the joyful song of now
eternally.

1989

ARKANSAS MOON

There once was a spoon
that rocked out a tune
to flatter & swoon
an Arkansas moon

Then it joined with a fork
& played hard like work
with ambition to park
in an Arkansas heart
This heart was kept safe
by a spry little waif
who's fun quickly doubled
when the spoon turned to bubble
with songs, games & humour
& poetry & art
these three had more fun
than a good healthy fart

Seestar & Wishter & Little Joy Blue
on colours, sounds & feelings
through eternity flew
not always together, but never apart
& that's how it was
right from the start.

1988

TERRA-RIFFIC

I'm shrieking through life
I'm shrieking through life
I'm shrieking through life
I'm shrieking through life
I'm shrieking through life
I was just born, now I'm 10 years old
I was just born, now I'm 20 years old
I was just born, now I'm 40 years old
& I'm shrieking through life
I'm shrieking through life
I'm shrieking through life
I'm shrieking through life
Earth spins 20,000 miles a day
Galaxy spirals, I can't venture to say
Universe is expanding at a pace
that keeps withstanding
the omnipresent pressure
of infinity
& I'm shrieking through life
I'm shrieking through life
I'm shrieking through life
I'm shrieking through life
I'm shrieking through life
I'm shrieking through life
I'm shrieking through life
All the material that I perceive
is piling up around me

turning into debris
while my thoughts keep wondering
how to explain
Life as a human
on this terra-firma plane
& I'm shrieking through life
I'm shrieking through life
I'm shrieking through life
I'm shrieking through life
I'm shrieking through life
I'm shrieking through life
I'm shrieking through life.

1989

LOVE SONG IN ENGLISH FOR YOU (GILLIAN'S SONG)

I'd like to sing the words I Love You
in a language known only by you
I'd like to create the fantasy
you always dreamed your lover would do
I'd like for us to have the freedom
to be surprised whenever we meet
& though I hunger for your presence
with your love my appetite's replete

I'd like to know you as a sister
to share any space & time
I'd like to offer you whatever
your heart desires of mine
It's the song that is essential
not the words, the rhyme or the tune
You see my love is existential
& to try to tell it just runs to ruin
You see our love it just exists
& to try to tell it just runs to ruin

1989

PEACE

I'm a radioactive
mercenary junkie with AIDS
I tempt the temptations
laugh at death to its face
You've got to love me
if you follow the teachings of Christ
You've got to love me
if Krishna's your spice
You've got to love me
if you take Buddha's advice
You've got to love me
if you *really* think you're nice

I'm a radioactive
mercenary junkie with AIDS
I'm your worst bloody nightmare
I tempt the temptations
laugh at death to its face
    PEACE

1989

UNLOCK MY FUTURE

    Bars, bolts, locks & latches
    Computerized key, combination that matches
    Fences of iron, walls of stone
    Keeping all out, staying in alone

Weapons of fear
preaching profits of freedom
all the time thinking
that doom will besiege them
Destroy, mutilate, trained to kill
for the master

Alarm, alarm, the kind thinking
bypasser.

Protection, speculation
That's the name of the game
Never mind harmonizin'
just project that they'll steal
the papers, the jewels, the money, the art
With all the paranoia
the real thieves have a head start
  The real thieves
  The real thieves
  The real thieves
take your energy in exchange for your brain
teaching us fear, calling it sane
manufacturing the toys
as a by-product to sell
in exchange for the monetary note
we earn so well
  The real thieves
  The real thieves
  The real thieves
manufacture & distribute
that monetary note
that's worth about as much as
your dreams of freedom
kept locked up in fear of a
human goat

Freedom is not a commodity
Freedom is an expression
If you want it,
you live it regardless of the situation
I don't want my great great great grandchildren
children that I'll never meet
raised in a society that professes freedom
standing at a podium of fear
I don't want my great great great grandchildren

children that I'll never meet
born behind
    Bars, bolts, locks & latches
    Computerized key, combination that matches
    Fences of iron, walls of stone
    Keeping all out, staying in alone

1990

KINKY BUTT SHUFFLE

No matter how glorious the body
No matter how talented the moves
Feels like 2 part masturbation
if it ain't got that off beat groove

I'm grateful for the sensation
I'm grateful for the sensation
I'm grateful for the creation
of our intimate relation
You have my adoration
I even have your admiration
but before we climb into that bed
let's climb into each other's head

& if it's lovers we're to be
let's think sensitivity
& when I look into your eyes
it's you I love to see, not me
in disguise as me
through your eyes

No matter how glorious the body
No matter how talented the moves
Feels like 2 part masturbation
if it ain't got that off beat groove

Yo! Take it personal
but don't take offense
I really think you're beautiful
but sex is so intense
Let's make love all day long
with every other glance
Thinking social harmony
while we redefine romance

No matter how glorious the body
No matter how talented the moves
Feels like 2 part masturbation
if it ain't got that off beat groove

I'm grateful for the sensation
I'm grateful for the sensation
I'm grateful for the creation
of our intimate relation

1990

The Storm Justifies the Building of a Shelter

ID I.D.

Hi. My name is Fraction
It's just a fraction of my identity
You can call me that, but it's not what I call myself
I don't need a name to separate me from someone else
I think of my self in thoughts
that only sometimes come in words
I know who I am without the auspices of a name
Why call you by name when it's you I'll remember,
not a word
Your identity, you see
is as abstract to me
as your image would be
for me to paint
on a canvas of air
with a paintbrush of words
using colours you can only hear
Hi. My name is Fraction
It's just a fraction of my identity
You can call me that, but it's not what I call myself
I don't call myself
I'm never that far away.

1990

I KNOW YOU KNOW ME

I have a vision of you that you don't see
& I can't see me the way you do.
I'm a reflection of everything I've ever experienced
& while I'm seeking myself
you already know me
& while I'm influencing you
& you change to reflect me
we get attached to the drama
in the space that separates we
That's a definition of one
in the company of many
the process of time
& the illusion of identity.
(I'll say it again . . .)
I have a vision of you that you don't see
& I can't see me the way you do.
I'm a reflection of everything I've ever experienced
& while I'm seeking myself
you already know me
& while I'm influencing you
& you change to reflect me
we get attached to the drama
in the space that separates we
That's a definition of one
in the company of many
the process of time
& the illusion of identity.

5/92

FORMULA

I'd like to write a meaningless song
An international hit, about 3 minutes long
With all the necessary instrumentation
I could set myself up for 3 generations

All I need is the formula
Just the perfect CON FORM ULA

With a love scene & hate scene
& some casual lifestyles
With nostalgia & romance
& occasional violence
With distractions & reactions
But avoid any mention of silence

I'd like to write a meaningless song
An international hit, about 3 minutes long
With all the necessary instrumentation
I could set myself up for 3 generations
All I need is the formula
Just the perfect CON FORM ULA

7/90 – 2/91

CAN'T SETTLE FOR LESS

When you can't settle for less
it makes for such a lonely world
But if you hold out for more
there's even more in store

Whatever you imagine is possible
as possible as nothing at all
When you can't settle for less
hold out for more
Whatever you imagine is possible
as possible as nothing at all
When you can't settle for less
hold out for more
(short song, eh?)

3/92

JOAN (BAEZ) & JANE'S (FONDA) SONG

I'm going out of my mind,
it's coming out of my mouth
straight through my heart
& it's tearing me apart
I don't want to think it, just want to sing it
don't want to rehearse it, just want to converse it
  with you
don't want to create it, just want to relate it
don't want to debate it, just want to elate it
  with you
I'm living in the center of infinity
traveling through a state of equality
seeking a sense of acceptance for me
  from me
My ego always wants
My mind is always content
My love is never spent
Now if I could conjure up some confidence
I'd be an asset to my constituents

Songs, games & humour & the joy to be alive
When it gets down to the bottom line
  that's how we will survive
Though death & misery abound
bombs are bursting all around
songs, games & humour & the joy to be alive
When it gets down to the bottom line
  that's how we will survive.

8/88 & 5/90

BASIS OF WISE

I saw a man with no legs
beyond his knees
& only one arm

dancing for tips, if you please
the man had charm
The bag lady bought *me* a cup of coffee
the other day
A 6 year old with leukemia smiled my way
Even soldiers with the grief of genocide in their eyes
have sung to me that joy is the basis of wise
joy is the basis of wise
You can seek, gain, contemplate & intellectualize
But I've got to realize
joy is the basis of wise
you see, cuz

My life has been damn good
Would you want me to hide it
My life has been so damn good
I wanna sing about it, I wanna shout it

Everybody pays some dues
just comin' out of the womb
& nobody gets away
without a trip to the tomb

My life has been damn good
Would you want me to hide it
My life has been so damn good
I wanna sing about it, I wanna shout it

Everybody's got a history
Everybody's got a story to tell
Every life is a mystery
if it's worth a whisper
it's worth a yell

My life has been damn good
Would you want me to hide it
My life has been so damn good
I wanna sing about it, I wanna shout it

1/92

CRY

I wanna learn to cry again
The one language we all understand
the first language we learn to use
the one language that bleeds the truth
I wanna learn to cry again
I wanna cry for humanity
s'got more potential than dignity
I wanna cry for the joy we've known
but even more for the shame we've shown
I wanna learn to cry again

There's more value in our tears
than our anger & fears
If you think you've been hurt
I put you on alert
When we can't smile back when someone
smiles at us first
& a cup of clear water won't quench our thirst
When we've destroyed the vegetation
that cleans the air
& we're lookin' for friends
but there aren't any there
We're gonna learn to cry again

I wanna learn to cry again
The one language we all understand
I wanna learn before it's too late
I wanna remember how to celebrate
I wanna grin so hard tears fall like rain
I wanna learn to smile again.

5/92

TERRATORIAL BEAST

Am I a terratorial beast,
or a civilized human being?
Am I a terratorial beast,
or a civilized human being?

Our intrinsic value's not measured by
the property we acquire
more by the love that we aspire
Civilization's what we require.

Am I a terratorial beast,
or a civilized human being?
Am I a terratorial beast,
or a civilized human being?

Livin' on the streets
happy I got a good sleep
beats drivin' to work
cursin' the creep
Knowing I don't own earth
beats thinkin' I do
& there's no bloody difference
between me & you

Am I a terratorial beast,
or a civilized human being?
Am I a terratorial beast,
or a civilized human being?

3/92

INTEGRITY

You know what scares me?
Well, it's not black people,
or skinheads,
or cops,
or dirty lookin' longhairs on their motorcycles chopped
It's not communities of Asians
or farm truckloads of "aliens"
or the drug-addicted loser
that lives outside the law
or the lady executive cruiser
with a gun beside her bra
You know what scares me?
The IRS
& the US Department of Immigration
The FCC
The FDA
& the Federal Reserve Corporation
not to mention the IMF
that turn a would be democracy
into an incarcerated nation
United Corporate Estates
transforming a cultural melting pot
into a fragile glass
of filtered water
bland
homogenous
& arrogantly naive
You know what scares me?
You know what *really* scares me?
YOU TRUST THEM
NOT ME

10/90

SON OF ABUSE

I don't live on the streets
I was raised in a mansion
From my head to my feet
I comply with the fashion
I'm scared to death
but wear a guise of ribald
Been beaten, laughed at or left
since I was 3 days old

I'm a son of abuse
I'm a son of abuse
I'm a discompassionate son of abuse
I've got a lightnin' quick fuse
for you I've got no use
forget about a truce
I'm a son of abuse

They kept me harnessed & leashed
never held my hand
Somethin' inside tells me
I don't wanna be a man
I've learned there's only one way
through this jungle of life
that's aggressive destruction, struggle & strife

I'm a son of abuse
I'm a son of abuse
I'm a discompassionate son of abuse
I've got a lightnin' quick fuse
for you I've got no use
forget about a truce
I'm a son of abuse

I've never been independent
Taught to comply, not decide
My concepts & instincts

may never coincide
Been schooled to intimidate
mislead & confuse
I'm a self promotin' candidate
  a son of abuse

    I'm a son of abuse
    I'm a son of abuse
    I'm a discompassionate son of abuse
    I've got a lightnin' quick fuse
    for you I've got no use
    forget about a truce
    I'm a son of abuse

1/92

NATURALLY

    The heart is broken, but the love remains whole
    naturally, naturally
    The heart is broken, but the love remains whole
    naturally, naturally

I took away your independence
stuffed it away in a bus
I swear there was no harm intended
I truly thought I was thinking of us
But I changed, you know
I changed, you know
I changed, you know it's true, I love you
But you're in love with another man
& I'm supposed to understand
after 10 whole years together
you're telling me there's someone better
You took nothing of me to remind you
but you're everywhere I turn
You're just leaving me all behind you

I feel as small as a shriveled earthworm
After all that I've done wrong
I suppose I deserve all this
We've been together for so long
How can I think positive
when everywhere I go
everyone wants to know, where are you?

The heart is broken, but the love remains whole
naturally, naturally
The heart is broken, but the love remains whole
naturally, naturally

5/87

RUTH'S SONG

She said, "Your love is so precious
I really think you'd enjoy
being loved by you"

Yo! I hear you my friend
& I'd like to surrender
to being loved by me

I forgive myself
Now my heart is wide open
to being loved by me
Cuz I know how it feels
to get high on the grief
& I don't need that pain
anymore now I see

She said, "Your love is so precious
I really think you'd enjoy
being loved by you"

Winter/91

THANK YOU TERRY ROSARIO

He didn't want to die
He just wanted some attention
He didn't want to die
He just needed some affection

He wanted to be a man
get away from mom & sis
17, drunk & in the can
on his birthday he'd enlist

A boy with high ideals
surrounded by men avoiding the real
aspects of everything
while all he ever really wanted to do was sing

A lesser among his peers
Identity lost within a whirl
of drunkenness & gambling debts
& would he ever kiss a girl?

Fight, gamble, get laid & get high
"If that's what it takes to be a man
I don't even want to try"

He didn't want to die
He just wanted some attention
He didn't want to die
He just needed some affection

He hung himself one night
when the drama got just right
They cut him down unconscious
& carried him to bed
"UNSUITED FOR MILITARY DUTY"
is what his General Discharge read

He lived to write this poem &
beyond concepts & misconcepts of right & wrong
I can tell you

He didn't want to die
He just wanted some attention
He didn't want to die
He just needed some affection
Thank you Terry Rosario
for saving my life

2/90

WANT, DESIRE OR PRAYER (???)

I want to write some childlike fantasies
I want to draw
I want to seduce the heart of humanity
the body of mother nature
& the mind of the great unknown
I want to rest my head on the breasts of youth
while being held in the arms of maturity
I want to sip the nectar of surrender
& surrender in return the passion I've confined
I want to help take my lover to orgasmic glory
while I remain in unspent peace
& together collapse
to breathe & ponder
the energy
we
re-
lease

9/89

LOVE IS SO ABSTRACT

Love is so abstract
Emotions are so intangible
They arrive like an attack
not always understandable
I don't ever want to be compared
but I always want to be the "best"
When will I ever learn
Having sex is not a test
it's another form of communication
However dear & intimate
a multisensual conversation
with ultravital intent

Love is so abstract
Emotions are so intangible
They arrive like an attack
not always understandable

It's best to be detached
from possessiveness of any kind
It's too difficult to find peace
in that fearful state of mind
So what's the matter with me
Why don't I live what I espouse
It's a wonder to me that I'm allowed to stay around

Love is so abstract
Emotions are so intangible
They arrive like an attack
not always understandable

I don't have to "win" your love
it's ours & always has been
To win or lose is all guess work
to know is harmonizin'

Love is so abstract
Emotions are so intangible
They arrive like an attack
not always understandable

3/90

MISSING YOU

I love missing you
as much as I love kissing you
cuz it reminds me of the sis in you
that stirs up the bliss in me

The sweet pain when you're not here
is like the sweet pain when we're so near
that our passion creates the fear
that we might forget to breathe

I've got my life
& you've got yours
When we're together
we have our inner course
& when we're separate
we have the memory
mmm. . .mmm. . .mmm. . .mmm. . .mmm

I love missing you
as much as I love kissing you
cuz it reminds me of the sis in you
that stirs up the bliss in me

3/92

KID'S STUFF

I'm sick & tired of the blues
Perpetually down & it's all bad news
If I've got another breath to take
let it be happy for goodness sake

I don't deny that there's war
grief, pain & poverty to be sure
But if I can put a smile on the face
of the child within,
it ain't no disgrace & it ain't no waste
I'm sick & tired of the blues
Perpetually down & it's all bad news
If I've got another breath to take
let it be happy for goodness sake

I suppose you think I'm an airhead
NAIVE, optimistic & so misled
But I'll keep on singin' till I'm dead
You may not revere it
but you don't have to fear it

I'm sick & tired of the blues
Perpetually down & it's all bad news
If I've got another breath to take
let it be happy for goodness sake

WHAT DO YOU THINK MEANS WAR
BUT THE ABSOLUTE ABSENCE
OF PEACE ANYMORE

WHAT DO YOU THINK MEANS WAR
BUT THE ABSOLUTE ABSENCE
OF PEACE ANYMORE

There's no age limit to being a "kid"
If you've got one more *bit* of knowledge to git

then you're somewhat innocent
& still a child
Embrace it, celebrate it
It's a waste of time to berate it
It's enchanting
That's why I'm ranting

I'm sick & tired of the blues
Perpetually down & it's all bad news
If I've got another breath to take
let it be happy for goodness sake

10/90

SOCIAL RAP

I'm a socializer, not a womanizer
I'm a socializer, not a womanizer
I'm a socializer, not a womanizer
I'm a socializer, not a womanizer

Sure I hug the sisters
& smile their way
but I hug a tree the very same way

Cuz I'm a socializer, not a womanizer
I'm a socializer, not a womanizer
I'm a socializer, not a womanizer
I'm a socializer, not a womanizer

I don't deny my hormonal instincts
but aggressive pursuit really stinks
If I wanna get close
I give the sister some slack
I mean who do I look like, Paul Black?
NOT!!

I'm a socializer, not a womanizer
I'm a socializer, not a womanizer
I'm a socializer, not a womanizer
I'm a socializer, not a womanizer

BREAK!!

The sun doesn't set, the earth rotates
How many years will it take to relate?
She's not a wo*man*, she's a womb person
Come on get your vocabulary straight
Sisters & brothers, don't you know we're the same
When we're acting like friends
we disregard the frame

BREAK!!

I'm a socializer, not a womanizer
I'm a socializer, not a womanizer
I'm a socializer, not a womanizer
I'm a socializer, not a womanizer

Now I know y'all get my drift
& appreciate the gravity of it
so when the brother's rap
gets a sister's frown
chill your act & prove you're really down
& be a socializer, not a womanizer
be a socializer, not a womanizer
be a socializer, not a womanizer
be a socializer, not a womanizer
Come on with me now

I'm a socializer, not a womanizer
I'm a socializer, not a womanizer
I'm a socializer, not a womanizer
I'm a socializer, not a womanizer

8/92

THE BRIBE

You'd better put me on the stage
or I'm gonna take the street
& if you leave me to the street
ain't no tellin' who I'll meet
You'd better keep me behind
these box office bars
cuz for what I've got in mind
you'd rather me be a star

Cuz I'm a flirtatious brother
& I'm tempting my fate
& might meet your mother
& she just might relate
You'd better put me on the stage
& keep me safe & secure
give me the funds that I need
& just a little bit more
You'd better satiate my appetite so I'll keep quiet
cuz if you leave me to the streets
I just might stop your riot
your damned earth riot
I've got the energy, you see, to draw attention to me
& while you're babbling away mindlessly
some sensible people might decide to be free
from your energy vamping bloody tyranny

You'd better put me on the stage
or I'm gonna take the street
& if you leave me to the street
ain't no tellin' who I'll meet
You'd better keep me behind
these box office bars
cuz for what I've got in mind
you'd rather me be a star

1/91

NY/SEA. IN ALASKA

Pen in hand
Heart in my throat
Sailin' through
this life that I wrote

Desirable friend
near at my side
seems like we're all
just along for the ride

Return to Alaska
after 43 years
the place of my birth
but I can't find the tears
Transitioning from
"I wish" to "I am"
the next card I draw
could be the image of PAN

Provocative songster
with a love for romance
I'm so grateful darling sister
that you joined in the dance
    Yes You

8/92

THE CRUX OF SURVIVAL

There's a word spelled FUCK
Rhymes with yuk
There's a word spelled SHIT
Rhymes with twit
There's a word spelled DAMN
Rhymes with dam

There's a word spelled GOD
Rhymes with odd
There's a word spelled CENSOR
Rhymes with sensor

The complex organism humanity
has 5 perception senses
plus 1 common sense
spelled INTUITION
Rhymes with inhibition

SHIT! I mean GODDAMNIT!
WHAT THE FUCK ARE WE AFRAID OF?
Do we really want to censor what we
see, speak & hear
leaving only touch & taste free?
ASK NINA HAGEN & PEE WEE HERMAN
about touch censorship
& how does irradiated food really taste?
Humanity is more than 2 generations old
We have survived. Life is evident of survival
Earth & nature are nothing to be afraid of
Anger & joy are natural expressions
When we're angry we swear—GODDAMNIT!
When we're full of joy we reproduce. WE FUCK.
THAT'S THE CRUX OF SURVIVAL

8/92

UNDER THE INFLUENCE

I'm under the influence
I'm under the influence
I'm under the influence
I'm under the influence
I'm under the influence
I'm under the influence

How can I conjure sobriety
when every single incident
is influencing me
Lust, music & all that I've consumed
Food, beverage & toxic fumes
Desire, ambition, failure & loss
Is my freedom to express truly accessible
& if so, at what material cost?

I'm under the influence
I'm under the influence
I'm under the influence
I'm under the influence
I'm under the influence
I'm under the influence

Familial, cultural, environmental
philosophical, theosophical, governmental too
Hereditary by nature
conditioned by impositions
these are the bases of my identity
Isn't it the same for you?

I'm under the influence
I'm under the influence
I'm under the influence
I'm under the influence
I'm under the influence
I'm under the influence

Perhaps you don't like the performance
It's only a performance
I could maintain constraint
& not smear the paint
or bend the notes
or address the issues
but

I'm under the influence
I'm under the influence
I'm under the influence
I'm under the influence
I'm under the influence
I'm under the influence

8/91

YOU'RE NOT MISSING ANYTHING (BUT YOURSELF)

You're not missing anything
anything but yourself
You're not missing anything
so forget about anything else

Architecture, agriculture
mathematics & entertainment
self-torture, human culture
& health & wealth attainment
Expressed to the ritual extent of a fit
you'll find
All paths course with the grace of God
but only your path leads to you

You're not missing anything
anything but yourself
You're not missing anything
so forget about anything else

All paths course with the grace of God
but only your path leads to you

3/92

SONG TO MYSELF (NO GUILT)

There are no simple solutions
but there are some difficult ones
If you're thinking in terms of disillusions
take a closer look at the moon & sun
There's trash on the moon
& the sun's got blemishes
What you're thinking is perfect
is only a nemesis
you're clinging to your grief
like the eternal victim
If you want to make a change
You've got to make an offering
of blood, sweat & tears
from the body that you're living in
& pray to yourself
that you learn to be forgiving
while we work for the joy
that's naturally our way of being
There are no simple solutions
but there are some difficult ones.

4/92

LAST WORLD ORDER: BANISH DENIAL

Education & communication
Dedication & determination
Organic integration without organization
Ozone rejuvenation
Corporate criminal incarceration
For rehabilitation
Cold war trials
Nuremburg style
Restore dignity to humanity
No more apathy

No more tyranny
Two laws
Celebrate life
Respect EARTH

6/92

NUT IN THE KITCHEN

LA LA LA LA LA LA LA
LA LA LA LA LA LA LA
LA LA LA LA LA LA LA
LA LA LA LA LA LA LA
Listen to the children sing
They can teach us everything
Let them play their games of war
They know they don't know
They know they don't know
They know they don't know what they're fighting for

They're survivors
revivers
keepers of the world of enchantment
They're transcenders
& remember
There's another one inside every one of us

Listen to the children sing
They can teach us everything
Let them play their games of war
They know they don't know
They know they don't—at least they *know*
They don't know what they're fighting for.

LA LA LA LA LA LA LA
LA LA LA LA LA LA LA
LA LA LA LA LA LA LA
LA LA LA LA LA LA LA

LA LA LA LA
LA LA LA LA
Listen to the children sing
They can teach us everything

9/91

STATE OF PEACE

Should I come upon a state of peace
would I support it or begrudge it
its comparitive relationship
to the rest of the world of grief?
I just wanna know
should I come upon a state of peace
would I support it or begrudge it
its comparitive relationship
to the rest of the world of grief?

1991

MARNII

Dear, sweet, delicious Marnii
me wishes I could charma
kiss away from you
Dear, sweet, romantic inspiration
fills me with infatuation
all day long I think of you
want to write a song for you
perhaps a poem will do
All day long I think of you

You're not perfect in my mind's eye
I guess I'm glad you're not
If you were

I'm sure my passion
would be ridiculously hot
You're a lovely urban flower
hard on the surface, soft within
splashing colours all around your world
like you were their origin

Dear, sweet, delicious Marnii
me wishes I could charma
kiss away from you
Dear, sweet, romantic inspiration
fills me with infatuation
all day long I think of you
want to write a song for you
perhaps a poem will do
All day long I think of you

The world is just a marketplace
You shop until you find
the food to nourish, the tool to service
the thought that satisfies the mind

Your poetry
You're poetry
Your poetry is what you are
You seem caught between
a divine routine
& arriving there by car

Dear, sweet, delicious Marnii
me wishes I could charma
kiss away from you
Dear, sweet, romantic inspiration
fills me with infatuation
all day long I think of you
want to write a song for you
perhaps a poem will do
All day long I think of you

I'd pour my heart out to you Seestar
But it's no longer so abandon
My conservative fears
in these middle years
have stifled that enchantment

Dear, sweet, delicious Marnii
me wishes I could charma
kiss away from you
Dear, sweet, romantic inspiration
fills me with infatuation
all day long I think of you
want to write a song for you
perhaps a poem will do
All day long I think of you

5/90

GOD CONCEPT

Is my concept of God laughing at me?
Is my concept of God angry with me?
Is my concept of God superior to me?
Is my concept of God equal to me?
It's my concept, It's my concept, It's my concept
Is my concept of God acceptable?
Is my concept of God definable?
Is my concept of God ineffable?
Is my concept of God conceivable?
It's my concept, It's my concept, It's my concept
Is my concept of God the great unknown?
Is my concept of God to be atoned?
Is my concept of God a concept alone?
Is my concept of God really my own?
Is *your* concept of God really different?
Is *your* concept of God really reverent?
Is *our* concept of God our deliverance?

It's a concept, It's a concept, It's a concept

If 10 billion people have ever lived
there's 10 billion facets on the conceptual jewel
of the manifest essence of "GOD"
& I only have access to potentially view
100% of one facet

1990

50/50 (SONG FOR CROW)

Guitar on my ribs
Drum on my back
Can't tell my head
From my hi hat
Feet going stomp, crash, boom
Please won't you stand back & give me some room
    I'm imprisoned again by my own foolish schemes
    Call it Hillbilly Willy's weight-loss machine
    I've tried fasting on coffee & minin' for rocks
    Even cut off my hair, my beloved dreadlocks
    But nothin's ever kept me so scrappy & lean
    As Hillybilly Willy's weight-loss machine

I'm aching to please, I'm aching to sing
I'm aching to get rid of this miserable thing
NAH! I don't really mean it
It's my own kind of humour
I thrive on the pain, but don't you start any rumours

    I'm imprisoned again by my own foolish schemes
    Call it Hillbilly Willy's weight-loss machine
    I've tried fasting on coffee & minin' for rocks
    Even cut off my hair, my beloved dread locks
    But nothin's ever kept me so scrappy & lean
    As Hillybilly Willy's weight-loss machine

Now the last time you saw me
I was drivin' a truck
Maybe this time you're thinkin'
I'm down on my luck
Well, don't you be worried & don't be concerned
All the money I've made is just energy burned.

I'm imprisoned again by my own foolish schemes
Call it Hillbilly Willy's weight-loss machine
I've tried fasting on coffee & minin' for rocks
Even cut off my hair, my beloved dread locks
But nothin's ever kept me so scrappy & lean
As Hillybilly Willy's weight-loss machine

9/89

MUTUAL ILLUSION

I've never met a messiah
but then I never met Lincoln
So don't roll your eyes up
cuz you know that I'm thinkin'
we share something divine
even though I can't define it
in your terms, in your terms, in your terms

You think I'm singing to you?
Well, I'm not. I'm singing to me
You teach me what I know
I turn it into poetry
present it in a show
emanating SOCIAL HARMONY

GRATITUDE, GRATITUDE, I know we're all grateful
Still I hunger for a plate full
of peace & tranquility
that still nurtures our vitality

encouraging us to sing
anything & everything
knowing that it's all to bring
some calm to the confusion
of our mutual illusion
that life is as we perceive it to be

I've never met a messiah
but then I never met Lincoln
So don't roll your eyes up
cuz you know that I'm thinkin'
we share something divine
even though I can't define it
in your terms, in your terms, in your terms

2/90

THANK YOU FOR YOUR TOLERANCE

I apologize to all the sisters
for my lust & desire
for the violence
where there should have been silence

I apologize to all you brothers
for my jealousies & fears
For my provocative way
giving bullies their day
I apologize to Earth
for my outrageous arrogance
to think I could live
without communion with plants
soil
water
weather
animals
& elements

I apologize to you
for taking advantage of you
in these shows that I do
But more than all this
I wish to express
my gratitude.
THANK YOU FOR YOUR TOLERANCE

7/92

SAYA CINTA DI BALI

Mungkin hidup mimpi hanya
Rasanya sama saya di Bali
Mungkin Bali mimpi hanya
Tetapi hidup indah sakali di Bali

Semua mata mau hanya senyum
Dan musik ada yang hidup
Dunia dan hidup ada cantik
Tetapi Bali sesuatu lagi
Sayaboleh tidak pernah tinggal di Bali
Meminta maaf untuk ketololan saya
Tetapi cinta di Bali
Saya cinta sungguh—sungguh di Bali

Mungkin hidup mimpi hanya
Rasanya sama saya di Bali
Mungkin Bali mimpi hanya
Tetapi hidup indah di Bali
Saya sungguh—cinta di Bali

4/92

AN OMNI-TACTILE SENSUAL VISION

You're too beautiful to be shy with
I imagine disassembling you
with the tenderest pressure
using only my palms
& placing the parts in the many
various pockets
of my "birthday suit"
& feel you reassemble
through the interconnecting network
of tunnels on my skin.

9/92

CAN OPENER
for Jim Page, October 1991

Contemporary troubadour
A fly in the ointment
of apathetic status quo & political appointment
of corporate geeks
to run the show

He opens the can of worms
with guitar, pen & a voice
& an expression that confirms
we all live with the choice
to be a can opener
to be a can opener
to be a can opener
or let the label
like a fable
mislead us to conform
& believe there's only nourishment
sealed tight
inside a can of worms

Contemporary troubadour
he opens the can of worms
with guitar, pen & a voice
& an expression that confirms
we all live with the choice
to be a can opener

ANONYMOUSLY ME

When I die I'm gonna take my legacy with me
When I die I'm gonna take my legacy with me
I'm gonna save the world anonymously
So you can thank yourself, but you can't thank me
With each translation very little remains
So you can have the achievement,
But you can't have my name
Cuz when I die I'm gonna take my legacy with me
when I die I'm gonna take my legacy with me

You might think that's very arrogant of me
to save the world anonymously
But you'd think the same if I claimed the fame
So you can have the achievement
but you can't have my name

Cuz when I die I'm gonna take my legacy with me
When I die I'm gonna take my legacy with me

I wish Krishna & Buddha & Jesus & Mohammed had done the same
Who needs the name
Life's still the same

So when I die I'm gonna take my legacy with me
When I die I'm gonna take my legacy with me

I'm gonna save the world anonymously
So you can thank yourself, but you can't thank me

With each translation very little remains
So you can have the achievement
but you can't have my name
Cuz when I die I'm gonna take my legacy with me
When I die I'm gonna take my legacy with me
When I die I'm gonna take my legacy with me

10/92

TO INSPIRE DIALOGUE

She said, "What kind of work do you do?"
Right in the middle of our show.
I said, "If you don't think this is work,
you try it"
Now
I wonder what she really meant.
Did she mean,
How do I suffer
to prove my faith
in a glorious "god"
as defined by another suffering human being?
She said, "The problem with freedom of speech
is
people like you
take advantage of it"
She also said she wasn't afraid of us.
I laughed
We were playing music
on a sidewalk
at a street fair
2 of us
Now
I feel proud

that she trusted us
& the audience of maybe 50 people
enough to express her
"freedom of speech"
as angrily as she did
& I wonder
would she have felt as fearless in the face of
the president
or any other politician
or a fear breathing evangelist?
I hope I meet her again
so I can thank her
for the honour she paid us
If you see her
tell her
She can interrupt our show anytime.

9/92

SONG FOR THE INNOCENT

I will fight no more forever
  So kill me

I cry immaculate tears at the birth of my child
  So kill me

I will not board your nationwide slave ship
  So kill me

I still sing & dance for life
While I mourn the unnatural strife
  So kill me

I'm the antithesis of a threat
  So kill me

My ineffable faith is none of your mortal business
  So kill me

Put a noose around my neck
Put your gun to my head
Deny my existence
Go ahead
Make me dead

Everybody suffers death in this place
You can die with dignity
Or you can die in disgrace

I will not support what I don't believe in
If the choices are profane
Then I have to contend
  So kill me

I will fight no more forever
The antithesis of a threat
I'll think for myself
I will not buy your debt
  So kill me

10/92

CONTEMPORARY VAGABOND

Ah! The sterile scent of dry dust
under the overpass
The sporadic thump-thump
of the traffic overhead
sorta lulls me to sleep
in my urban outdoor bed

    I feel safe, but vulnerable
    I feel alert, but relaxed

I don't owe anybody
& no one owes me
Don't want to hurt anybody
Hope no one hurts me
In this world of enchantment
I just want to live free
When it rains I get wet
When it's hot I just sweat

Like an alarm clock
the thumps are getting closer up above
Maybe today all the hate
will turn to love
Livin' outdoors ain't nearly as hard
as the grief I get for being a bard
All my lovers are sublime
& my children love me true
They're few & seldom seen
but what's a vagabond to do?

I feel safe, but vulnerable
I feel alert, but relaxed
I don't owe anybody
& no one owes me
Don't want to hurt anybody
Hope no one hurts me
In this world of enchantment
I just want to live free
When it rains I get wet
When it's hot I just sweat

I'm not guilty of the trespass
I'm so often accused
more the victim
than the instigator of abuse

The drugs, violence & deception
are just as plentiful
in the banks & the mansions
as on the streets
or under these transoms

10/92

SISTERS

Waitresses, bartenders & craftsisters
at the markets
Y'all pay me the highest honour.
You see all the creeps
You hear all the lines
You know all the passes
from all the guys
who are caught in the
perpetual abuse machinery
of this culture
this era
& you treat me nice
You regard me as a comrade
a brother
a sister's friend.
I've graduated
I've come through the other side
of the abuse membrane
& you have forgiven my falterings.

I'm grateful. I'm honoured.
You're so beautiful.

10/92

THE GRACE OF DIPLOMACY

Concepts are always ahead of actions
Communication of concepts can
frustrate manifestation
& so is the nature of future.

To be at peace with Now
is not complacency
if
tradition & innovation
are united in celebration
of the gradual process
of transition.

11/92

FREEDOM OF SPEECH?

In order to be allowed to voice
my perspective
& receive your conscious attention
I propose
that after listening
you have your own way.
I commit to this
to the point of
voluntarily perishing.
However
you must arrange the execution.

May I speak?

11/9

EBOLA ZAIRE

Ebola Zaire's a tropical filo-virus
Ebola Zaire's a tropical filo-virus
Ebola Zaire's a tropical filo-virus
taking 80 percent of it's hosts
in 10 days at the most
You'll be bleedin' from every pore
There's no tellin' how many more
hostless viruses exist
where there used to be rain forests
where there used to be rain forests
where there used to be rain forests

Where do you suppose all the animals go
when they chop down the rain forests?
Where do you suppose all the water will flow
when they chop down the rain forests?
Where do you suppose all the viruses go
when you chop down the rain forests
when you chop down the rain forests
when you chop down the rain forests?

Ebola Zaire's a tropical filo-virus
Ebola Zaire's a tropical filo-virus
Ebola Zaire's a tropical filo-virus
taking 80 percent of it's hosts
in 10 days at the most
You'll be bleedin' from every pore
There's no tellin' how many more
hostless viruses exist
where there used to be rain forests
The army has this one in Virginia
knowing someday it'll get in ya
If you don't believe me
take a course in immunology

11/92

WHY WRITE

I feel so incomplete & pensively poised
for a great collision with a due date
on my debts to universe
& I'm not prepared.
My accounts are in arrears.
I want to hide behind my passion
& bathe in desire
Swim in it
till it surrounds me & separates me
with eternity
from my fears
& to drown in it would invoke the greatest courage.
Yet here I stand
naked
on a shore
clinging to a towel of black ink
to cover my shame.

10/92

REVERSE ALIENATION

If I can't alienate everyone
I'm not gonna alienate anyone
If I can't alienate everyone
I'm not gonna alienate anyone
anyone at all

If I can't have my freedom of speech
I won't say a word & I won't be reached
If I can't have my freedom of expression
You won't get my thoughts & we won't get the lessons

If I can't alienate everyone
I'm not gonna alienate anyone
If I can't alienate everyone
I'm not gonna alienate anyone
anyone at all

If I can't have my freedom of religion
I'll contemplate the nature of that decision
If I can't relate to your matters of concern
I won't expect you to relate to mine in return

If I can't alienate everyone
I'm not gonna alienate anyone
If I can't alienate everyone
I'm not gonna alienate anyone
anyone at all

Some might say I'm ridin' a fence
Some might say that it makes no sense
Some might say they'd fight for the chance
while all I can say is I believe in the dance

Will Rogers never met a man he didn't like
when considering the source, I have no doubt
cuz I never met a person I didn't like
something about so
If I can't alienate everyone
I'm not gonna alienate anyone
If I can't alienate everyone
I'm not gonna alienate anyone
anyone at all

4/93

UNTITLED

Life is a glorious imposition
& the only alternative
is no alternative
at all
All minds pursue peace
as one's own identity
perceives peace to be

From the tyrant
to the sage
From the battlefield
to the stage
All minds pursue peace
as one's own identity
perceives peace to be

Acceptance, tolerance & forgiveness
for all transgressions
are the lessons
We're imposed upon to learn
as we earn
the glory of life
PEACE
PLEASE
I SURRENDER

1/92

SONG FOR DADDY

Spontaneous song by my daughter Roberta, age 4, 1974

Oh Daddy, Oh Daddy, Oh Daddy
Oh Dad please don't go yet
Oh Daddy, Oh Daddy, Oh Daddy
Don't step on any rocks oh Daddy
Oh Daddy, Oh Daddy, Oh Daddy
Close your eyes oh Daddy
Oh Daddy, Oh Daddy I got a surprise